First Time on a Plane

ParRagon

Bath · New York · Singapore · Hong Kong · Cologne · Delhi
Melbourne · Amsterdam · Johannesburg · Auckland · Shenzhen

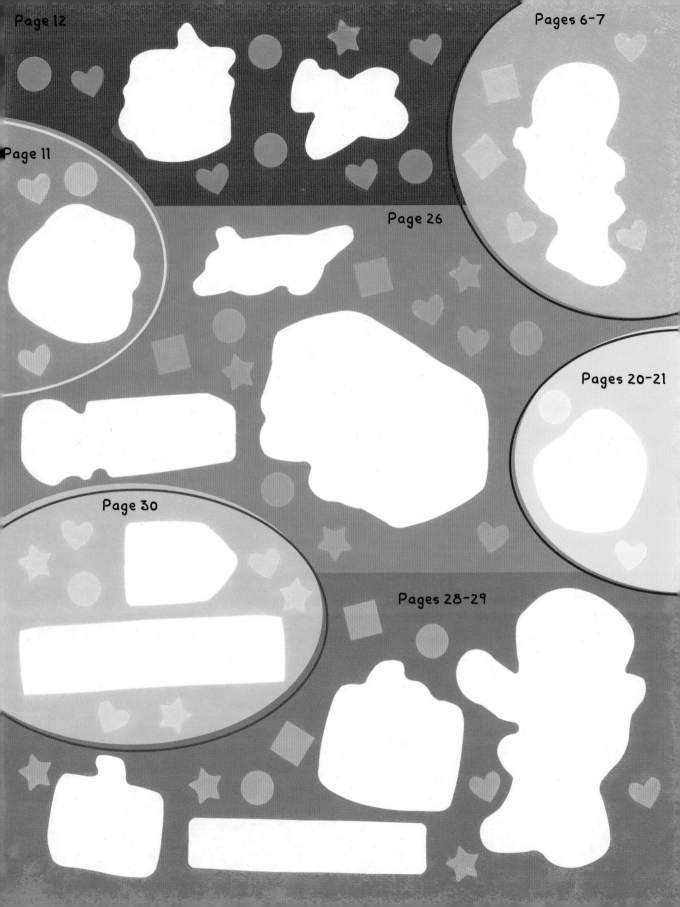

Page 12

Pages 6-7

Page 11

Page 26

Pages 20-21

Page 30

Pages 28-29

How to Use This Book

 Read the story, all about Dan going on a plane for the first time.

 Look at each picture in the story closely. You may be asked to find or count things in a scene and place a sticker on the page.

 Try each activity as you go along, or read the story first, then go back and do the activities. The answers are at the bottom of each activity page.

 Some pictures will need stickers to finish the scenes or activities. Any leftover stickers can be used to decorate the book or your things.

Dan and his mom and dad are going to visit
Aunt Lucy and Uncle Bill, who live across
the country in a different state.

Information

1 2 3 4

Can you find these things in the airport?

They are going there on a plane! They have just arrived at the airport, and there are lots of people all around.

First, they hand in their tickets at the check-in counter. Their bags get put on a baggage carousel to get to the plane.

What number check-in counter are they at?

The gate agent gives Dad their boarding passes, so they can get on the plane.

Follow the lines to see which suitcase belongs to which person.

1

2

3

Answer: 1, Mom, 2, Dan, 3, Dad.

At the security gate they put their bags in a tray to go through the X-ray machine.

Can you see Dan's teddy bear in the picture?

Can you find these things in the picture?

DEPARTURES

Then they walk through a metal detector.
Dad makes it beep!

DEPARTURES

Now place the sticker of Dan's backpack here.

The departure lounge is really busy with lots of shops and places to eat.

Mom buys Dan his own toy plane and they look out of the window to see what is happening on the runway.

Count the number of each thing below that Dan can see out the window.

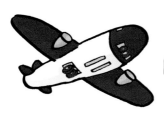

Planes

Suitcases on the ramp to the plane

People working on the runway

Flag

Red truck

Green truck

It's time to get on the plane! At the departure gate, a flight attendant checks their boarding passes.

Can you spot five differences between this picture and the one opposite?

Answer:

Everyone walks down a tunnel called
a jetway to get to the plane.

At the door to the plane, a flight
attendant named Sue greets them.
"Welcome aboard!" she says.

Help Dan find his way to the check-in counter, to the security gate, through the departure gate, and to the plane.

Answer:

On the plane, everyone sits down and fastens their seat belts. The engines make a loud whirring noise when the pilot starts them up.

Find the life jacket in the picture.

Sue shows everyone where the bathrooms are, and how to stay safe on the plane.

Which two pieces complete the image below?

a
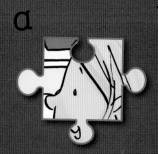

b

c

d

The plane takes off and they go higher and higher!

Can you point to the wheels on the plane?

Can you find these things in the picture?

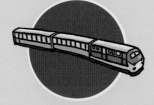

Outside Dan can see the trees, houses, and people getting smaller and smaller.

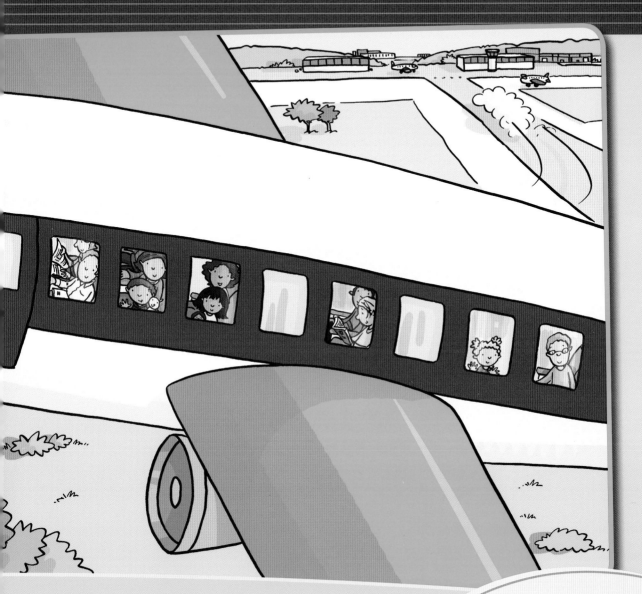

Now place the sticker of the pilot here.

It's time for lunch. A flight attendant comes down the aisle with a cart full of trays.

Which juice drink does Dan have?

Dan has chicken for lunch.
"It looks yummy!" says Dan.

Can you find these things in the picture opposite?

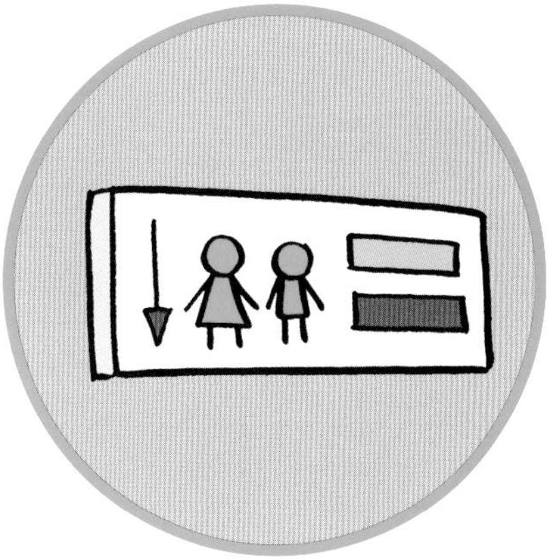

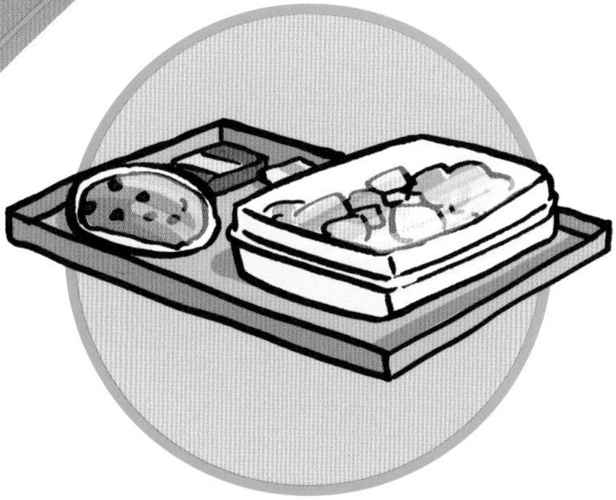

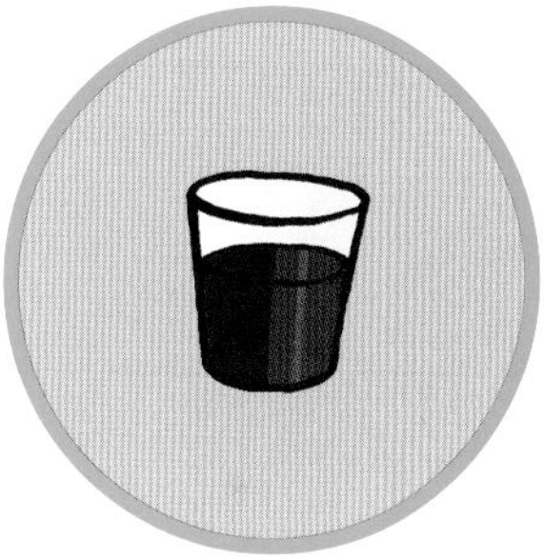

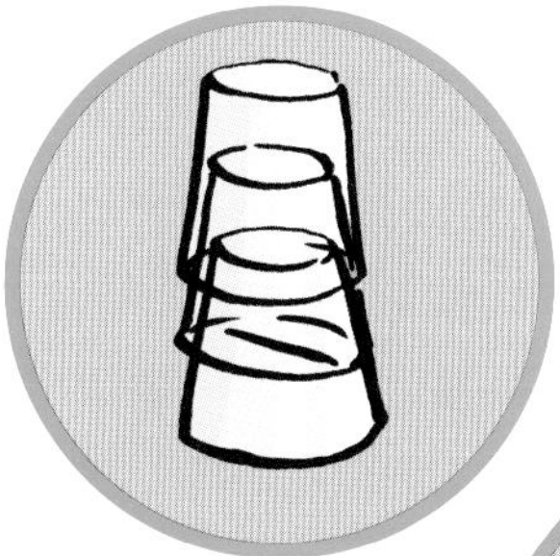

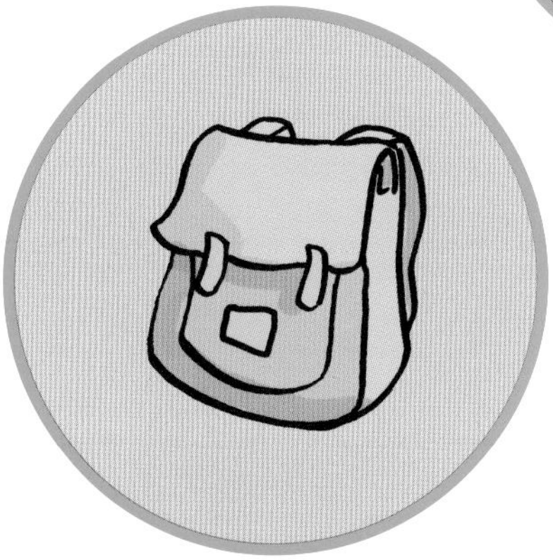

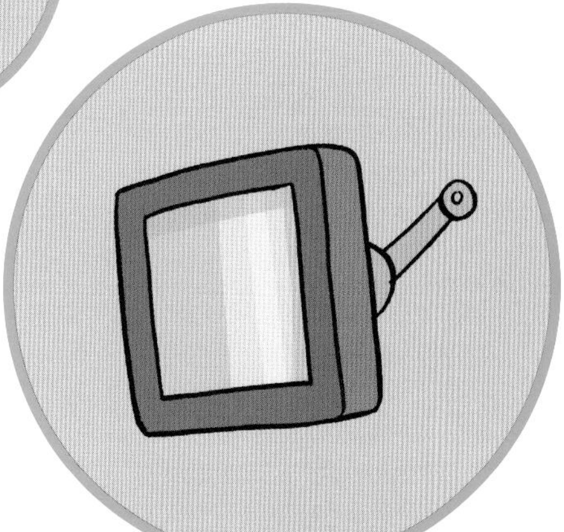

After lunch, Dan watches a movie.
He wears earphones to hear the sound.

The pilot tells everyone it's time
for the plane to land!

Look at the objects below. Find one in each row that is different from the other two.

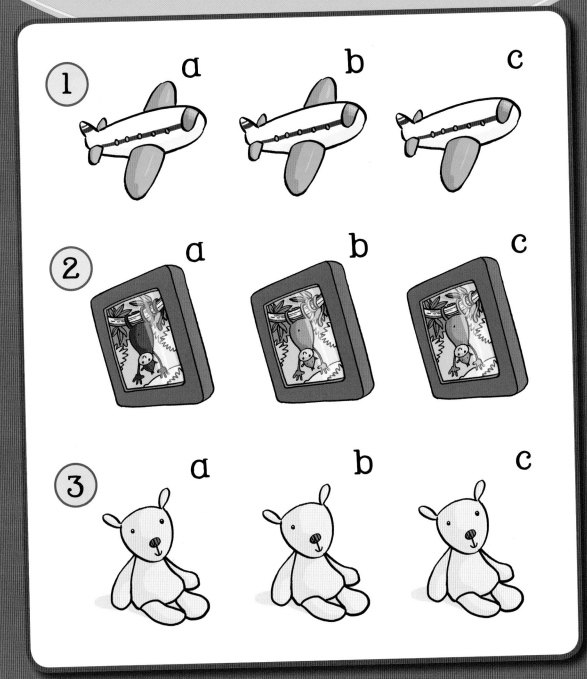

1   a   b   c

2   a   b   c

3   a   b   c

When the plane has landed, Sue says goodbye to the passengers as they leave the plane.

Find the stickers to finish the picture.

A bus is waiting to take them to the airport.

Can you match the objects and people to their shadows?

In the airport they head for baggage claim.
"There's my red bag!" says Dan.

Find the stickers to finish the picture.

Flight No: 1234

Can you find these things in the picture?

28

Dan helps Mom and Dad find their suitcases on the baggage carousel, too.

HELP DESK

Now place Dan's suitcase sticker here.

Outside baggage claim, Aunt Lucy and Uncle Bill are there to meet them. "Hello!" they say. "How was your flight?"

Find two stickers to finish the picture.

"It was great!" says Dan. "And we get to fly home, too. I can't wait!"